THE SECOND ONE AND ONLY COLOURING BOOK FOR ADULTS

The Second One And Only Colouring Book For Adults

ISBN: 978-1-907912-79-5

First published in English by Phoenix Yard Books Ltd, 2015

Phoenix Yard Books
Phoenix Yard
65 King's Cross Road
London
WC1X 9LW

1 3 5 7 9 10 8 6 4 2

A CIP catalogue record for this book is available from the British Library
Printed in Malaysia.

www.phoenixyardbooks.com

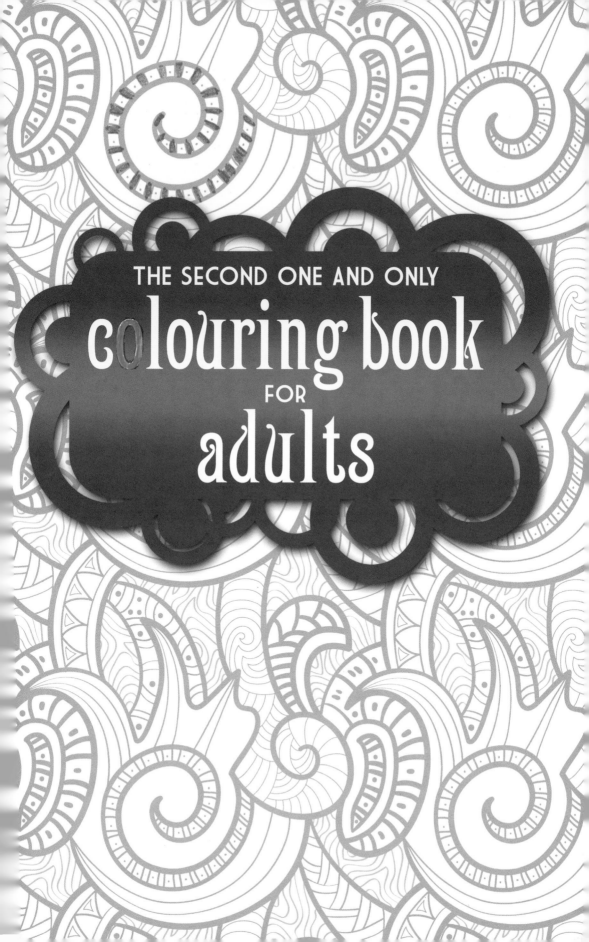

THE SECOND ONE AND ONLY

colouring book
FOR
adults

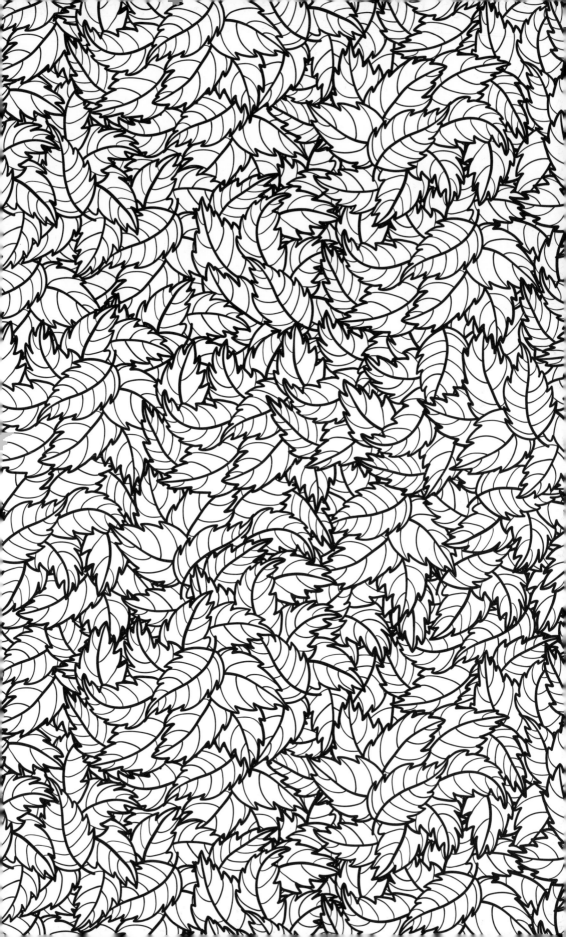

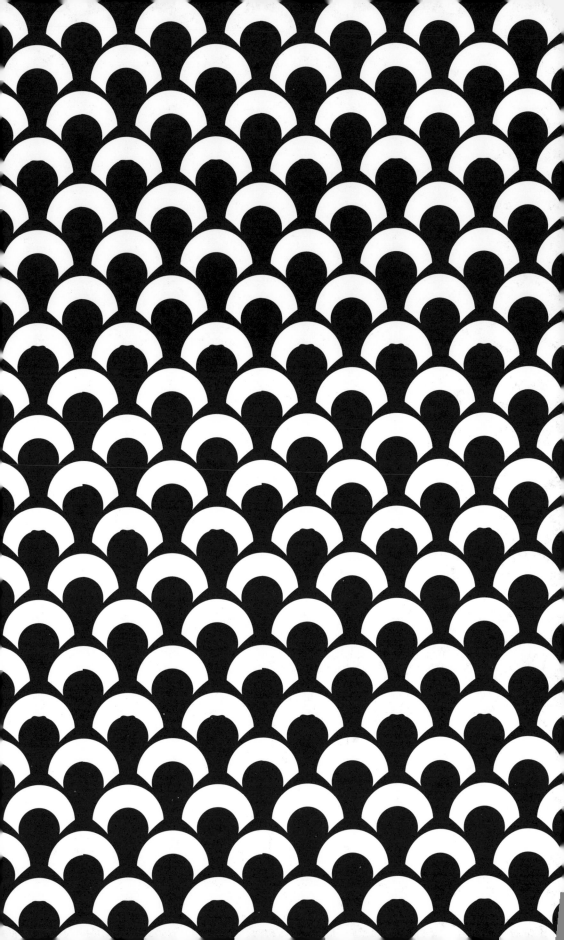

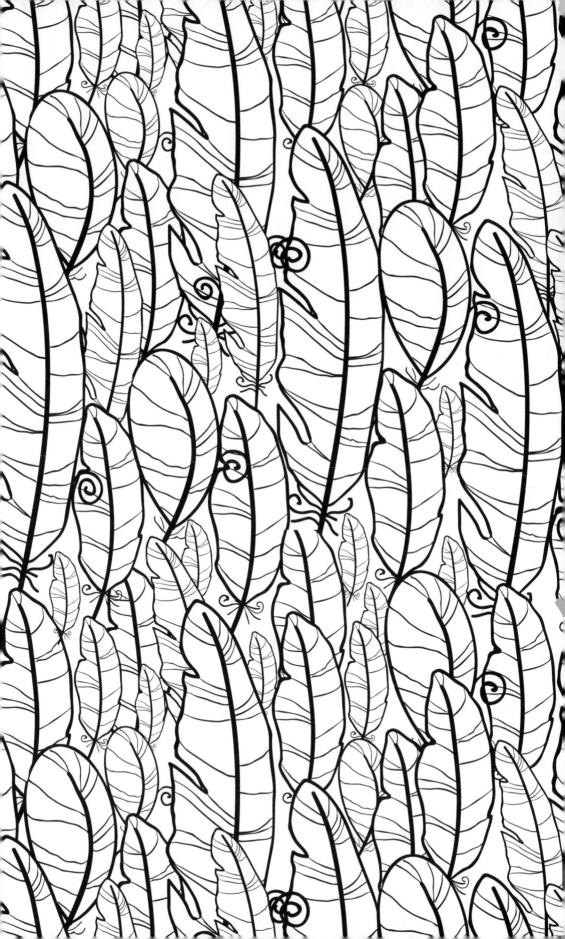

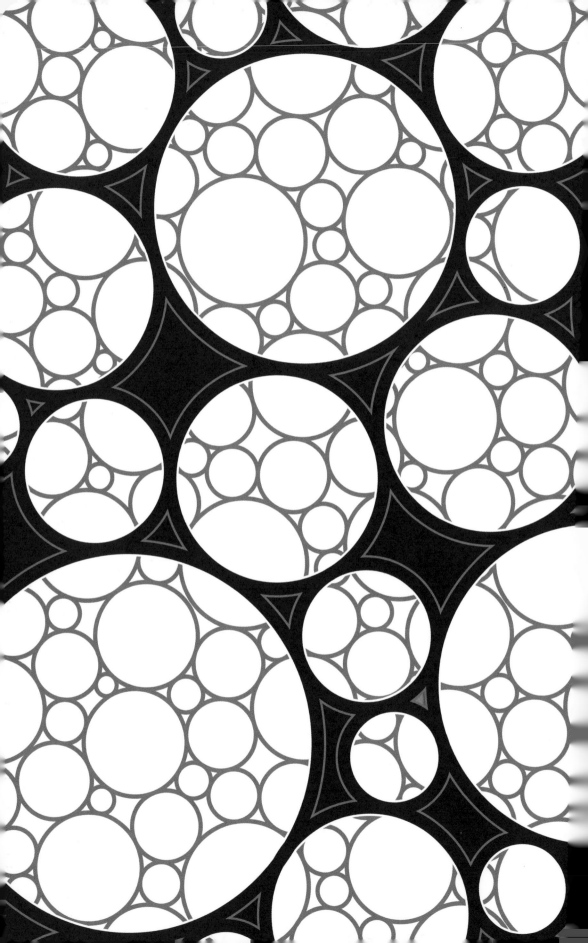

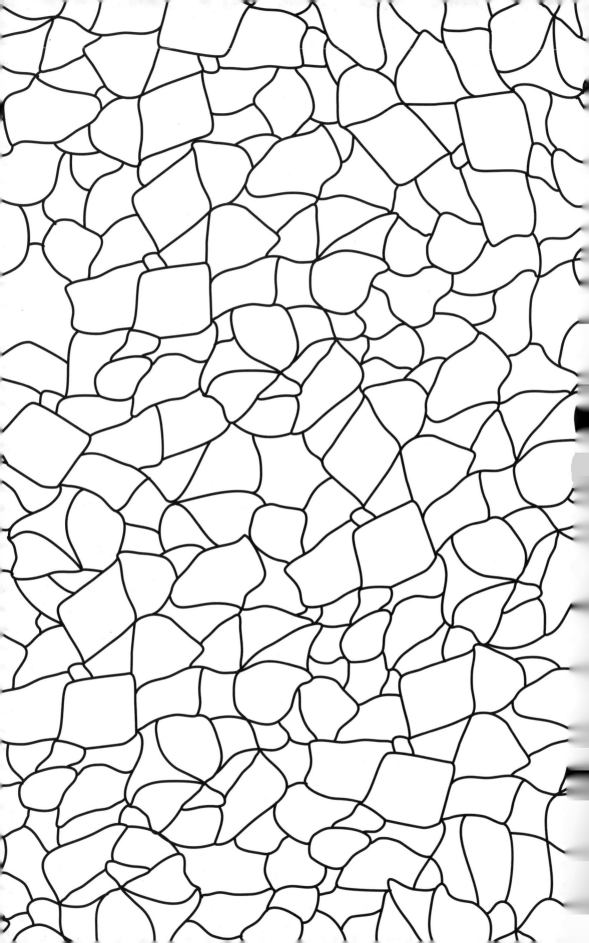